Oh, the Mountains You'll Ski

A Coloring Book Ski Parody

For everyone that loves the mountains in winter.

This book is especially dedicated to my children Bella, Gianna, & Marcello; and their Cousin Crew of: Coen, Marin, Kaia, Jessiah, Avonlea, Samuel, Maya, Marcus, Mari, Anthony, Jonus, Catherine, Jack, Justin, & Ethan. All My Cousins. Corbett, Major, Casey, and Violet too! Thank you for inspiring the best in me and reminding me that I could do it. Never stop chasing your passions ever. Ski the Bold Line!

To Grandma Maisie, thank you for always encouraging me to pursue my art and my adventures. It's been the greatest gift to be you and Gramps's grandson. To Mom & Dad, thank you for letting me be me and always encouraging me to play outside & to Jenni for always playing with me. To my wife GG, the hundreds of days spent skiing with our kids are beyond compare in my mind, thank you for your love, enthusiasm, and for always packing the snack bag. Thanks to the Fukatomi's for all the hand me down gear over the years. Aunt Deb, thanks for always being quick with a joke and never taking life too serious.

I'd also like to give a shout out to all my ski and slowboarder buddies & other friends for keeping the stoke alive in me over the years, on and off the mountain, in the current realm and in realms of the past still alive in the mind; including: Wes & Scotty, Debfed & Mrs. Debfed, Tod, Eric & Alyssa, BZ, Ken Dawg, All the JB's around the World, The Casady's. Fink, Thompson, Arthur, Patrick, Peter, Burton, Nicco, Nate, McCully, Colby the Eagle Scout, Ged, Joel, Eddie P. & Nicole, Keely & Spencer, Chris, Jordan B, Jordan C., The Nichols Sisters, Brother James, Anne, Nava, Geno & Lori, The Ivory's, Conor & Lindsay, Taylor & Lisa, Arave, Timmy & Crystal, Jojo, Clayton, Todd the Bod & all the Bealers, Topher, Zach, Johnny, Trav Dog, Tanner, Paul, Deryk, Shaner, Bamford, The Jones's, Danny, The Black Tornado Wildbunch Gang & The Dirty Dozen, All the Wild Girls from the 541, Waputi, The Duryea's, The Compton's, Baker Snowfield, Greg & Jen, The Poker Crew, The Highly Refined Gentlemen of 2nd Christiansen in Monmouth, OR. The WOU Monday Night Raw Crew, Ill Bill, The Supper Club Crew, Mike E. on the Drums in Denver, Cousin Kyle & Moose Dog, BBC, Garrett, Brian, Gorio, Nick B., Fat C, Slim E, Jared, Jake the Snake, Gordo, Davie, Jimmy, Jason, Jesse, Frankie, Badcock, Johnson, Brent & Summer, Brian & Shawn, Kelly, Kris & Chandra, Breno & Ashley, Aaron, Josh, Ben, Jed's Party, Lenora's Ghost, The Dudes from the Cadillac Ranch, The Snapple Baseball Team, Johnny Harr, The Fortmillers, Mean Dean, Colleen, KiKi, Yosh & the Ohana, The Primetime Sports Bar & Grill in Springfield, OR, Ray-Ray on the Beach in Maui, The Six Dog Night Race Crew, BunDiggity & All My Rowdy Friends from Estacada, and anyone else I ever caught a chair with!

Special thanks to Jack Hutt with CityLeague Ski Racing for the heroic effort in keeping racers of all ages racing 4-5 days & nights a week at Snoqualmie Pass, WA. Last but not least, thank you Uncle D for strapping skis on my feet in jeans all those years ago at Mt. Ashland, it's been downhill ever since!

Keep your tips up!
Dr. Chutes

WILDSIDE PUBLISHING   PACIFIC NORTHWEST, USA

Oh, the Mountains You'll Ski

A Coloring Book Ski Parody By Dr. Chutes

Ski With Us on the Web!
www.ohthemountainsyoullski.com

Published By:
WildSide Publishing
Bellevue, WA 98007
www.wildsidepublishers.com

Back Cover Photography By: Debra Federline at Whitefish, Montana

Coloring Book Edition
ISBN:979-8-9857694-1-8

Wahoo!
The snow is finally flying today.
It's up in the high places!
You must get up and get moving along on your way!

Your helmet will protect that brain in your skull.
Your feet will be buckled snug in your boots.
You can shift your weight on your edges
to go any which way you may choose.

You've scouted your line, at the top now ready to go.
Like a blur, you'll soon be swishing and swooshing through the freshly fallen snow.

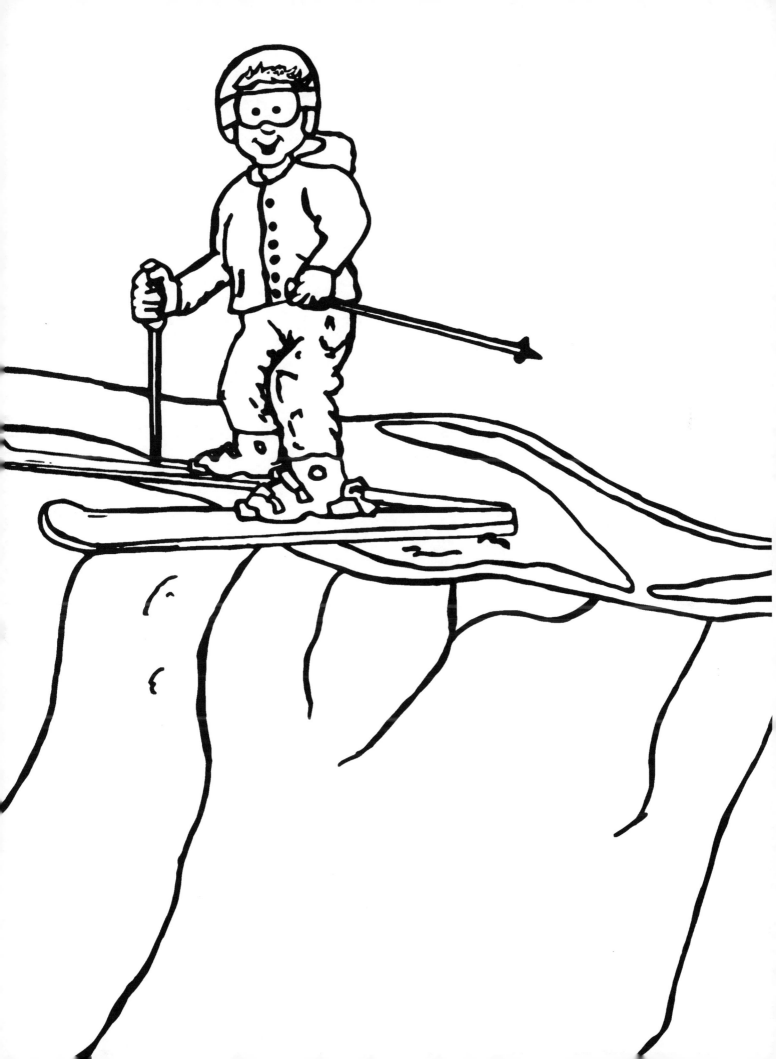

You'll find on your journey there are many of trails.
Always be sure to evaluate with great care.
If they're too steep or too rocky,
it's ok to say, "It's not safe to play there."
With your helmet full of wits and your feet tight in your boots,
you're far too clever to descend those most dangerous of routes.

Conditions can change,
and sometimes nothing may look fit for descent.
When this happens, you must go somewhere else,
where the snow isn't setting up like cement.

It's better up there
in the fresh mountain air!

Up there snowflakes start flying
every winter they do
for folks that are agile
and like to send it like you.

At first you may crash.
Don't get discouraged. Don't stop.
Bounce up, dust off, and soon enough
you'll be hitting the cliffs and the drops.

You'll get on a chairlift for a ride to the peak!
You'll survey the amazing views from the top!
You'll likely see others up there,
boarders and skiers preparing to drop.

You're fast as a rocket when you're skiing downhill.
You'll zoom past your crew like they're standing still.
Whatever mountain you're on, you'll be faster than fast.
Whatever route you take down, you'll rarely be passed.

But it's bound to happen every now and again.
Because others have skill and they want to win.

It pains me to say it
but, regrettably, it is correct
that Ski Fails
and Yard-Sales
may leave you with a kink in your neck.

You may find yourself perched
on top of a craggily face.
Your legs will be shaking.
And your heart it will race .

It may take some courage to get down from that face.
Just take it one turn, one turn at a time.

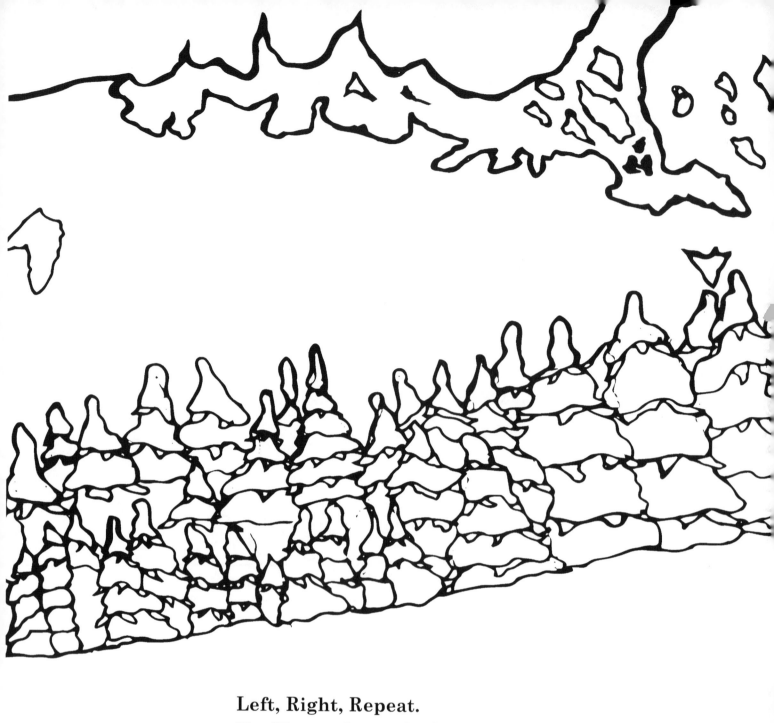

Left, Right, Repeat.
You'll soon be at the bottom just fine.

Always ride with a friend and ski in control,
to avoid launching yourself right off of the run.
For tree wells, steep slides, and bruisy bumps
are never much fun.

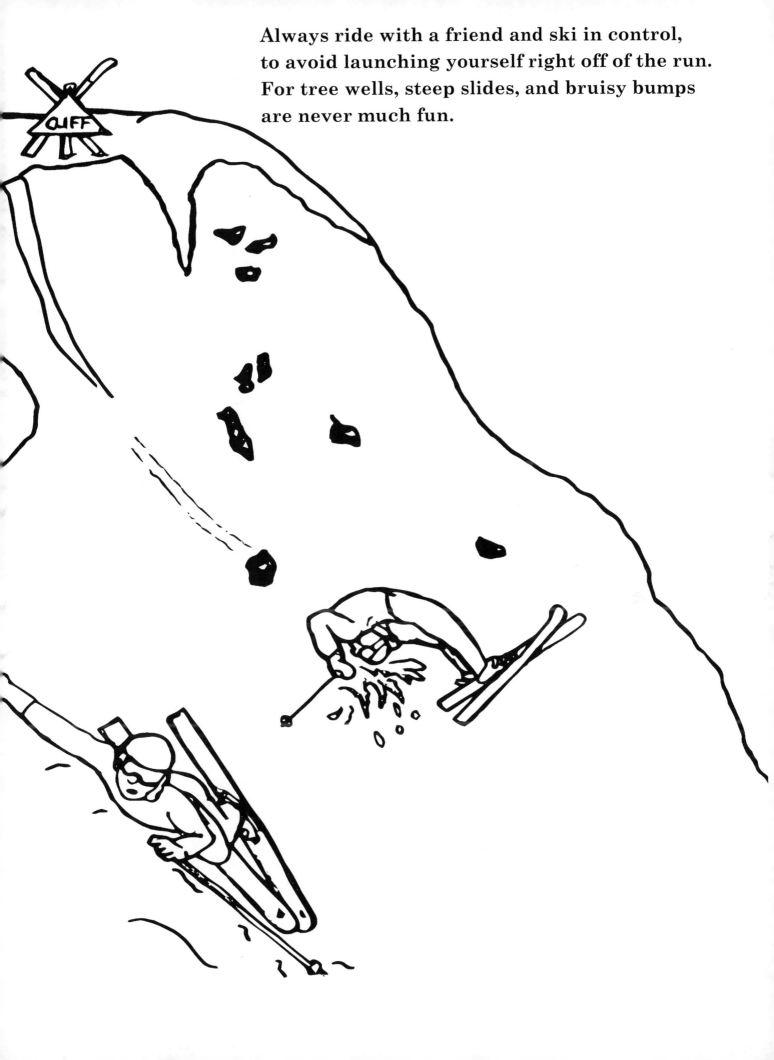

You may arrive on a slope where the runs aren't on the map.
Some trails look enticing, but they could be a trap.
A trail that could take both your life and your limb!
Dare not duck a rope line, enter only through the gates!
Ask yourself always , "Is the risk worth whatever treasure awaits"?

For safety comes first out there in Avalanche Zones
be it back country, side country, or even on steep cinder cones.
In that pack on your back three things should be carried
a shovel, probe, and a beacon, in case you are buried.
Choose your lines wisely, as Avalanches are scary.

It can be quite perplexing
out there in the wide open space
to rediscover the path that leads you back to your base.
You're safely back in bounds now, but fear grips your face
the chairs are not moving, and the line's stopped in place.
Unfortunately, you've just arrived at The Delayed Place...

...where time itself slows down.
Delayed for a bomb to blow
or 'cause the winds severe, or for the lights to glow
or to fix a gear, or a liftie to show,
or to render aid, or a rope to tow
or delayed for patrol just to say it's a go
or even delayed for just too much snow
Nothing is moving everything is delayed.

Delayed to make the cable tight
or delayed confirming conditions are right
or delayed waiting for the day to light
or delayed, maybe, for the ice to break
or to check the oil, or a due to a huge mistake
or the powers out, or to fix a safety bar
or they need a scout,
or something even more bizarre.
Nothing is moving everything is delayed..

NOPE!

Bad lift lines aren't for you!

With climbing skins on your skis you can break free
from all the standing and stalling.
To discover untracked glades,
where the freshest powder is calling.

On your face the cool wind's a whipping,
as you prepare for your descent from on high!
It's just you, the mountain, the snow, and the sky.
Like a bird on the wind you're ready to fly!

Oh, the Mountains You'll Ski! There is merriment to be had!
Fresh groomers with your family. Steep and deep runs with Dad.
All the marvelous ways you'll learn to move on those skis
as you dip, dodge, and duck though the gates and the trees.
Glory! You'll be as stoked as stoked can get,
If you're in the race, it's on you they'll bet.

Aside from when it's not
More often you'll find, the race is hard fought.

At times I'm afraid
you'll find yourself staring down a most difficult line.
A course you're not certain you can even complete.
A battle royale of mountain versus mind.

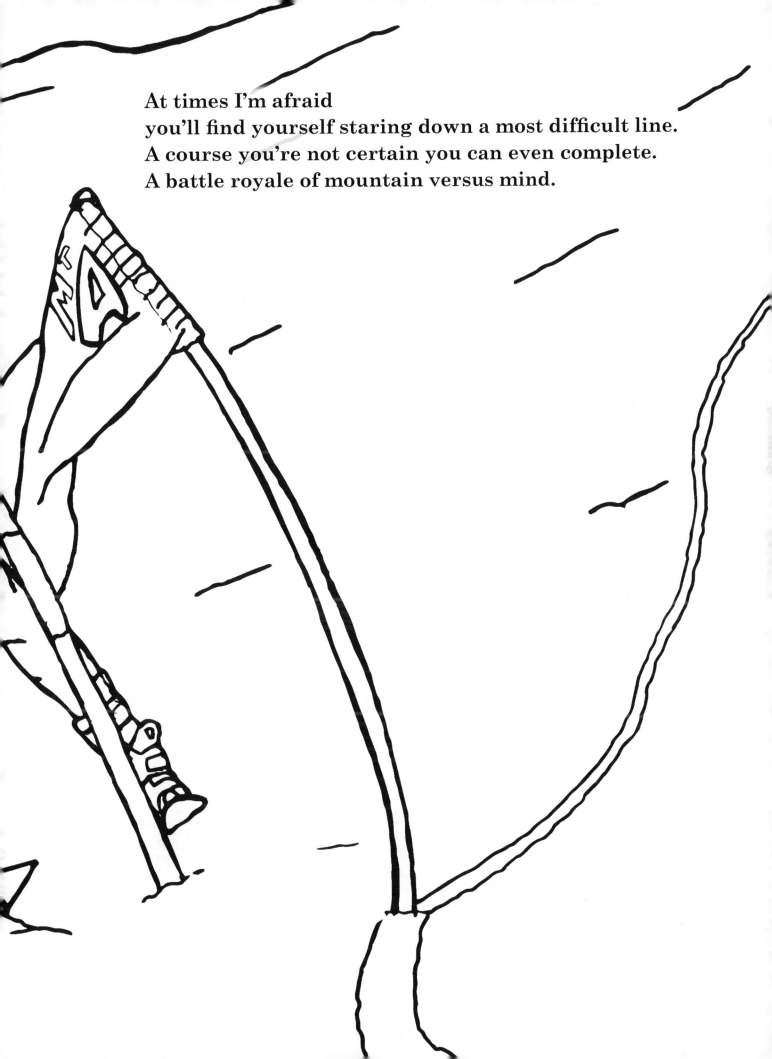

Nervous!
For better or worse,
the mountains can leave you feeling it
on a challenging multi-day traverse.

And in times when you're nervous, the odds are quite high
you'll feel butterflies in your stomach starting to fly.
There are lines in the couloirs between granite and ice,
that can petrify you with fear if you stop to think twice.

Onward you'll ski
through the wind and the rain.

Onward you'll ski
even when icy conditions create doubts in your brain.

Onward you'll ski
right through Hahnenkamm's terrain.
On ahead down many
a formidable line,
albeit your face may be frosty
and your sore legs they may whine.

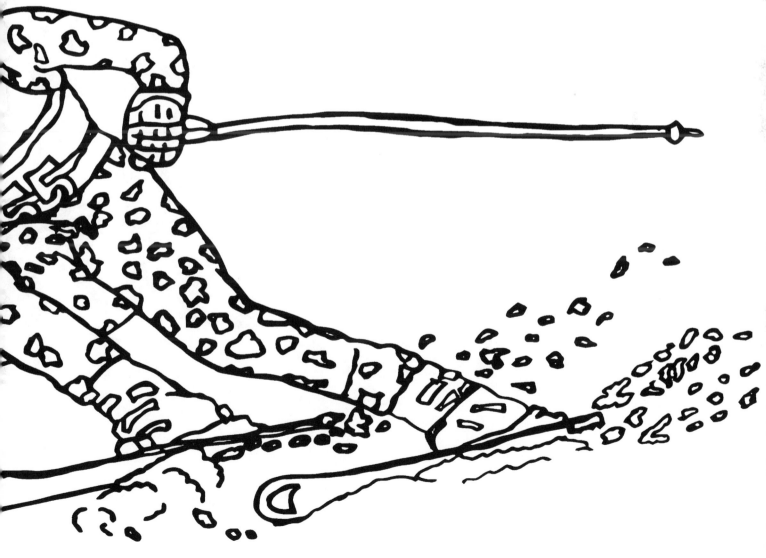

Time and again you'll hike up,
to the greatest of heights
and confront all the conundrums
that may be in your sights.

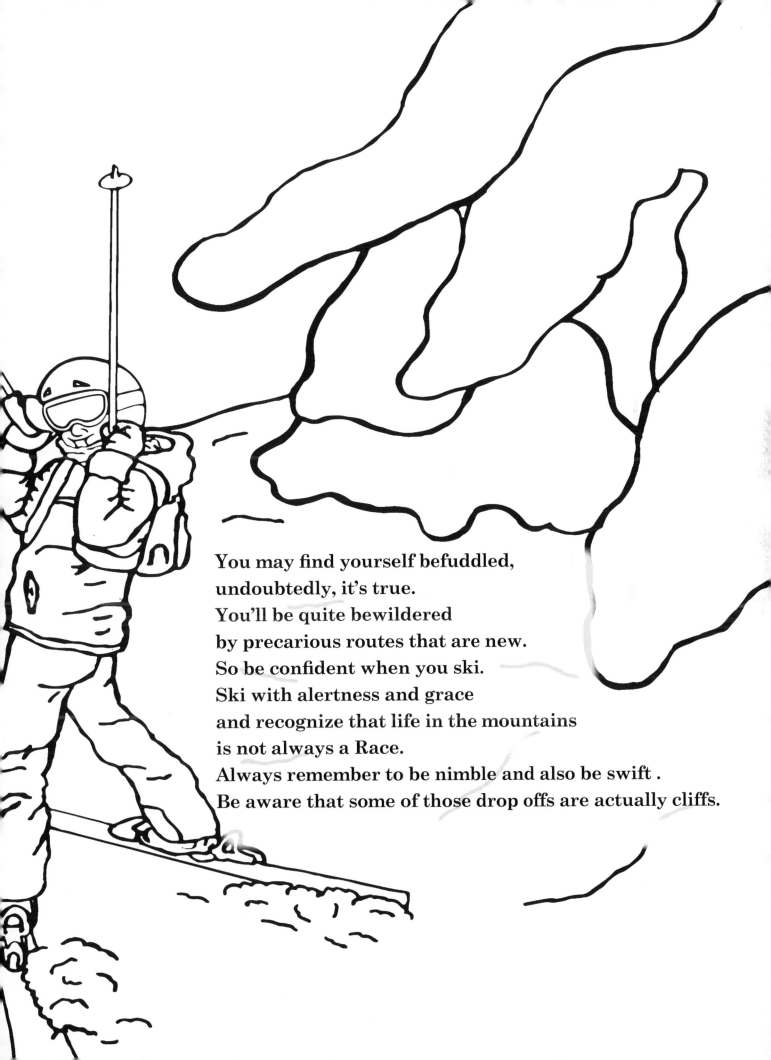

You may find yourself befuddled,
undoubtedly, it's true.
You'll be quite bewildered
by precarious routes that are new.
So be confident when you ski.
Ski with alertness and grace
and recognize that life in the mountains
is not always a Race.
Always remember to be nimble and also be swift .
Be aware that some of those drop offs are actually cliffs.

Will your life be better because you learned to ski?
Absolutely, You'll see!
(I give you a 110% percent guarantee)

KID, YOU'LL SKI MOUNTAINS!

So...
be the mountain Kitzbuhel or Courchvevel or Chamonix
or closer to home at The Summit at Snoqualmie,
You're ready for adventure!

Today is the day!
The Mountains Are Calling.
So...grab your skis
and get moving along on your way!

KID, YOU'LL SKI MOUNTAINS!

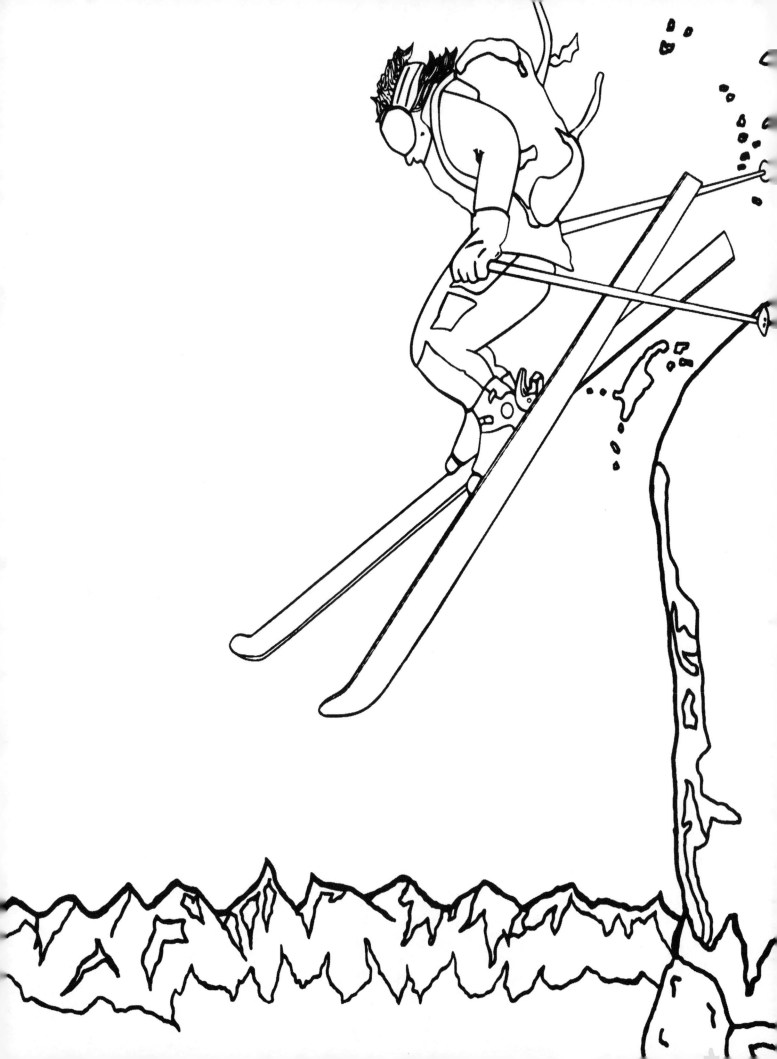

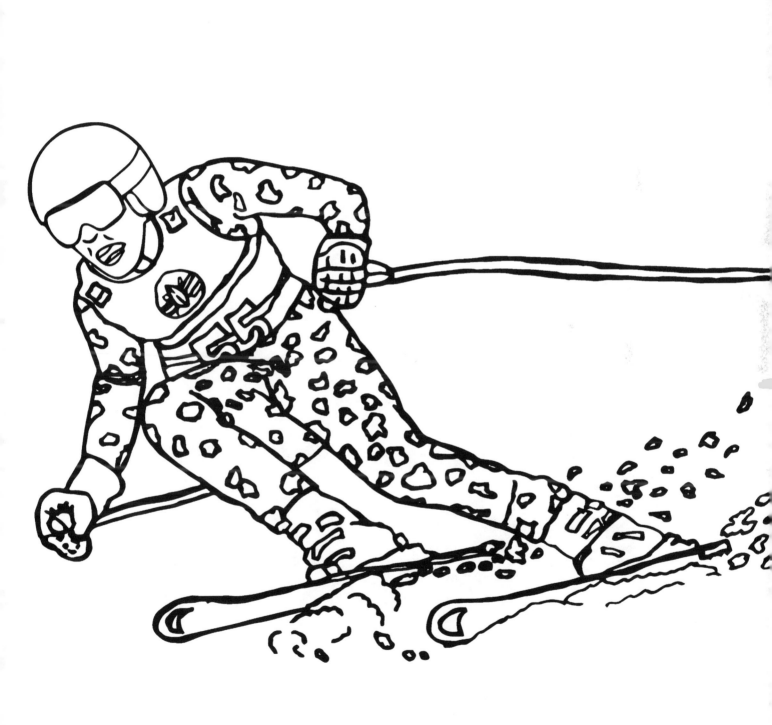

Made in the USA
Monee, IL
25 November 2023